11+

15-MINUTE PRACTICE PAPERS

Series editor Tracey Phelps, the 11+ tutor with a

96% PASS RATE

Maths

English

Verbal Reasoning

Non-verbal Reasoning

SCHOLASTIC

Published in the UK by Scholastic Education, 2020

Book End, Range Road, Witney, Oxfordshire, OX29 0YD

A division of Scholastic Limited

London – New York – Toronto – Sydney – Auckland

Mexico City – New Delhi – Hong Kong

www.scholastic.co.uk

1 2 3 4 5 6 7 8 9   0 1 2 3 4 5 6 7 8 9

British Library Cataloguing-in-Publication Data

A catalogue record for this book is available from the British Library.

ISBN 978-1407-18375-6

Printed and bound by Ashford Colour Press

Papers used by Scholastic Limited are made from wood grown in sustainable forests.

Author

Tracey Phelps

Editorial team

Rachel Morgan, Suzanne Holloway, Vicki Yates, Sarah Davies, Julia Roberts, Jennie Clifford

Design team

Dipa Mistry and Andrea Lewis

Illustration

Tracey Phelps

Contents

About the CEM Test 4

Practice Paper 1 5

Practice Paper 2 9

Practice Paper 3 13

Practice Paper 4 17

Practice Paper 5 21

Practice Paper 6 25

Practice Paper 7 29

Practice Paper 8 33

Practice Paper 9 37

Practice Paper 10 41

Practice Paper 11 45

Practice Paper 12 49

Practice Paper 13 53

Answers 57

Coverage chart and scores 60

About the CEM Test

About the CEM test

The Centre for Evaluation and Monitoring (CEM) is one of the leading providers of the tests that grammar schools use in selecting students at 11+. The CEM test assesses a student's ability in Verbal Reasoning, Non-verbal Reasoning, English and Mathematics. Pupils typically take the CEM test at the start of Year 6.

Students answer multiple-choice questions and record their answers on a separate answer sheet. This answer sheet is then marked via OMR (Optical Mark Recognition) scanning technology.

The content and question type may vary slightly each year. The English and Verbal Reasoning components have included synonyms, antonyms, word associations, shuffled sentences, cloze (gap fill) passages and comprehension questions.

The Mathematics and Non-verbal Reasoning components span the Key Stage 2 Mathematics curriculum, with emphasis on **worded problems**. It is useful to note that the CEM test does include mathematics topics introduced at Year 6, such as ratio, proportion and probability.

The other main provider of such tests is GL Assessment. The GLA test assesses the same subjects as the CEM test and uses a multiple-choice format.

About this book

Scholastic 11+ 15-Minute Practice Papers for the CEM Test Ages 10–11 offers authentic multiple-choice papers covering all of the key 11+ skills identified above.

This book contains:

- 13 15-minute practice papers, each containing 30 questions.

- Multiple-choice questions that reflect the different question types that are common in the CEM 11+ test, at a level appropriate for the age group.

- A coverage chart mapping the content of each test to the subjects and topics within the CEM 11+ test. Use this to identify areas of strength or weakness.

- Short answers are included at the end of the book. Extended answers are included at **www.scholastic.co.uk/pass-your-11-plus** or via the QR code below.

It is not expected that children will complete every timed test in the allotted time. Use the tests to develop test techniques and to gradually improve speed and accuracy as they get used to each question type. You might, though, wish to record how many questions your child is able to answer in each test and to work on increasing speed over time.

The following icons are used to allow you to identify the question types.

Shuffled sentences	Antonyms	Cloze	Pictures	Definitions
Comprehension	Synonyms	Maths	Word associations	Vocabulary

Practice Paper 1

 Instant replay

Was that a penalty? In today's fast-paced sports, action can be difficult to see. Since referees, umpires and linespeople are only human, they make mistakes. But such errors, unintentional as they arc, have affected the course and outcomes of many matches. Players, managers and fans complained about refereeing decisions. Something had to be done; technology, potentially, offers a solution.

5 In 2018, the Video Assistant Referee (VAR) system was inaugurated at an FA Cup match between Brighton & Hove Albion and Crystal Palace. Decisions became more accurate because football officials could analyse slow-motion video from several camera angles to reconsider and then overturn any incorrect decisions.

However, although some errors have been corrected because of this innovation, it has also led to complaints
10 about which incidents are reviewed, how long the reviews take and how reviews interrupt play. Some feel that the old problems have simply been replaced by new ones.

Tennis, another sport with long and honoured traditions, had similar issues with officiating. Line calls were contested vigorously by players. Spectators, justifiably so, were frustrated when bad calls were upheld. That ball was in! Umpires rarely changed their calls, so tennis officials acknowledged that changes in
15 officiating rules were needed.

Change came to the Wimbledon tennis championship in 2007 with the introduction of Hawk-Eye. This system uses camera angles to calculate the trajectory of the ball. Accordingly, questionable calls can then be reviewed and corrected. Hawk-Eye provides a reliable and impartial second opinion, but over use could become a problem. For that reason, players are only allowed to challenge three calls per tennis set.

Carefully read through the passage and circle the correct answers belows.

1 What consequences can refereeing mistakes have on a match?

A. They can help players to train differently.

B. The referee might decide to change the rules.

C. People will learn from their mistakes.

D. They can influence how the match goes and the final result.

---

2 How long after Hawk-Eye was first used was VAR launched?

A. 25 years

C. 18 years

B. 7 years

D. 11 years

/2

3   Which sport tried out the Video Assistant Referee system in 2018?

     A. Tennis

     B. Football

     C. Cricket

     D. Rugby

---

4   What happens when VAR shows that a mistake has been made in a football ruling?

     A. The incorrect decision is changed to correct it.

     B. The referee is changed.

     C. The players can decide what should be done next.

     D. Nothing – incorrect decisions cannot not be changed.

---

5   Which one of the following statements describes the writer's opinion correctly?

     A. The Hawk-Eye system cannot be trusted.

     B. Tennis is not very popular.

     C. Audiences are right to feel fed up about uncorrected mistakes in tennis matches.

     D. Technology can solve all the problems of mistaken sports rulings.

---

6   Which of the following could be used in place of 'trajectory' without changing the meaning of the sentence?

     A. Pathway

     B. Size

     C. Analysis

     D. Image

---

7   Which of the following would not be a problem if Hawk-Eye was used too much?

     A. Players could try to use it on every point they lose.

     B. It would get very boring for spectators to spend more time watching challenges than sport.

     C. Hawk-Eye could run out of power if people use it too often.

     D. It would slow the game down too much if players used it on every point.

/5

Look at the grid and write the answers to the questions in the boxes.

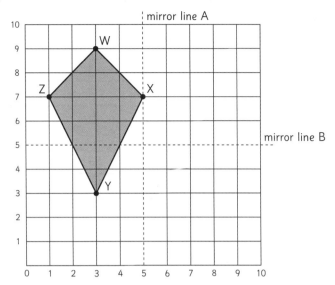

8 | What would be the coordinates of point W if it were reflected in mirror line A? | (☐ , ☐)

9 | What would be the coordinates of point Z if it were reflected in mirror line B? | (☐ , ☐)

10 | What would be the coordinates of point X if it were reflected in mirror line A? | (☐ , ☐)

11 | What would be the coordinates of point Y if it were reflected in mirror line A? | (☐ , ☐)

/4

Circle the word which has the most opposite meaning to the word on the left.

12	**conflict**	ceremony	harmony	acrimony	testimony
13	**horrible**	achievable	inevitable	remarkable	agreeable
14	**necessary**	conditional	occasional	operational	optional
15	**commence**	conclude	convince	confuse	concede
16	**acknowledge**	remark	promote	ignore	pledge
17	**change**	reserve	persevere	pretend	preserve
18	**familiar**	informal	strange	similar	infamous
19	**lethal**	useless	hapless	harmless	heartless
20	**subtle**	firm	precise	obvious	ironic

/9

Complete the sentences by circling the most appropriate word from the options A to E.

21 Aarti had skipped breakfast and lunch, and by late afternoon she was _____ .

A	B	C	D	E
haggard	skinny	famished	greedy	withered

22 The whole class became _____ in the exciting story the teacher was telling.

A	B	C	D	E
consumed	gripped	enthralled	intrigued	engrossed

23 The delayed plane finally made a _____ departure just before midnight.

A	B	C	D	E
belated	overdue	early	punctual	slow

24 Joseph takes a water bottle to school every day in order to stay _____ .

A	B	C	D	E
evaporated	hydrated	damp	parched	perished

25 Young Mollie cannot drink milk as she is allergic to all _____ products.

A	B	C	D	E
fruit	sugar	dairy	meat	poultry

/5

In each question below, the words may be rearranged to form a sentence. One word does not belong in the sentence. Circle the superfluous word from the options A to H.

26

of	can	recycled	household	turns	be	lots	waste
A	B	C	D	E	F	G	H

27

for	a	does	charity	work	Sue	went	voluntary
A	B	C	D	E	F	G	H

28

determined	Elliot	effort	finish	race	was	to	the
A	B	C	D	E	F	G	H

29

her	the	made	feel	walk	dizzy	ride	fairground
A	B	C	D	E	F	G	H

30

rock	howling	through	the	the	trees	was	wind
A	B	C	D	E	F	G	H

/5

Practice Paper 2

 In the following passages, some of the words are missing. Complete each passage by selecting the words from the options A to H. Each word may only be used once. Write the correct letter in each answer lozenge.

Passage 1

organs	survived	short	rigorous	rarely	lived	delicacy	typically
A	B	C	D	E	F	G	H

The fugu fish is considered a (Q1 _____) in Japan and is always eaten raw and served in thin slices. The dish is incredibly fashionable and expensive. Diners love to boast about having eaten fugu and (Q2 _____) the experience because a single fugu contains enough poison to kill 30 adults. To qualify as a licensed fugu chef, applicants must complete two full years of (Q3 _____) training under the close supervision of a master fugu chef. The chefs must learn how to prepare fugu, separating the highly poisonous (Q4 _____) from those that are edible. There is a two-hour written examination at the end of the course and (Q5 _____) only 20 per cent of applicants will pass. The successful chefs will then be fully licensed to serve fugu dishes in their restaurants, and are able to charge their customers over £300 each for the experience.

Passage 2

moaning	venue	lamenting	advance	swiftly	served	quite	offer
A	B	C	D	E	F	G	H

In 1970, the first branch of KFC opened in Japan, in the city of Nagoya. The restaurant (Q6 _____) became incredibly popular with the public, and several other branches were opened that same year.

A few years later, just prior to Christmas, one of the restaurant's managers, Mr Okawara, overheard a large group of Americans loudly (Q7 _____) the lack of turkey on offer in Japan during the festive season. Okawara responded with an ingenious idea: he arranged for a special 'party barrel' of fried chicken to be (Q8 _____) at his restaurant to celebrate the holiday. The idea was such a success that, nowadays, KFC has become the traditional (Q9 _____) for the Japanese to trek to for their Christmas lunch. People have to book months in (Q10 _____) for a table to avoid disappointment.

/10

Circle the odd one out from the options A to E.

11

 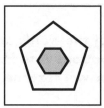 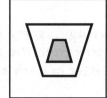 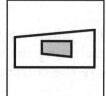

A · B · C · D · E

12

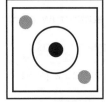  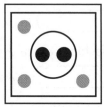 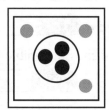 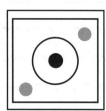

A · B · C · D · E

13

A · B · C · D · E

14

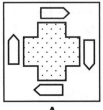  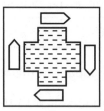 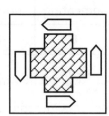 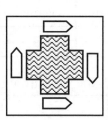

A · B · C · D · E

15

A · B · C · D · E

/5

In the following questions, circle the correct answer from the options A to E.

16 Ali shares £84 between his two children in the ratio 2:1. How much is the larger amount?

A	B	C	D	E
£28	£56	£38	£42	£50

17 What is $\frac{1}{8}$ as a decimal?

A	B	C	D	E
0.250	0.200	0.125	0.175	0.400

18 Which one of the following numbers is not divisible exactly by both 5 and 10?

A	B	C	D	E
6050	7880	3150	5270	4005

19 Trisha cycles 2.4km and then walks 450m. How far has she travelled altogether?

A	B	C	D	E
2.65km	2850m	2560m	28.5km	2800m

20 The perimeter of a square is 12cm. What is the area of the square?

A	B	C	D	E
16cm²	6cm²	7cm²	9cm²	8cm²

21 What is 43% of 400?

A	B	C	D	E
172	175	180	156	168

22 What is 58.084 rounded to 1 decimal place?

A	B	C	D	E
58.2	58.8	58.0	58.1	58.4

/7

Match the words to the correct definitions. Write the correct answer A to J in the spaces.

23	affection	
24	debris	
25	panorama	
26	remorse	

A   a story which contains a moral lesson

B   a wide view of an area

C   a disease in a part of your body that is caused by bacteria

D   a feeling of fondness for someone or something

E   a period of ten years

F   a feeling of regret about something that you have done

G   a funny musical play based on traditional children's stories

H   the scattered remains of something

I   a successful way of curing an ailment

J   something that makes you suffer

27	fluctuate	
28	reconcile	
29	hallucinate	
30	liberate	

A   to affect or change how something or someone develops

B   to see something in your mind which is not really there

C   to meet someone unexpectedly

D   to change all the time

E   to connect or fasten things together

F   to move continuously in one direction

G   to become friendly again after a fight or a quarrel

H   to think or believe

I   to set someone free

J   to make something more interesting

/8

Practice Paper 3

 Write the answer to each calculation in the boxes below.

1 A coach leaves Cheltenham bus station with 54 passengers on board.

10 passengers leave the coach when it stops in Oxford and 8 people board the coach.

12 passengers join the coach at High Wycombe and 8 passengers get off the coach. It then drives to London.

How many passengers are on the coach when it arrives in London?

2 Two hundred and forty passengers arrive at the airport for a flight.

The aeroplane is smaller than expected and only only 80% of the passengers are able to board the flight. The rest have to wait for the next one.

How many passengers have to wait?

3 Bridget and Aya have a total of 40 books between them.

Aya has three times as many books as Bridget.

How many books does Aya have?

4 In a survey of 120 people, 30 of them said they preferred to take the bus rather than the train.

If this data was to be shown in a pie chart, how many degrees would represent those people who prefer to take the bus?

°

/4

5   Patsy reads 18 pages of her book every day.

She starts her latest book on Tuesday and after her reading on Thursday, she still has 32 pages left to read.

How many pages are there in Patsy's book?   ⬜⬜

---

6   A small village school is presenting a play in the school hall.

All 32 children are there, along with some of their parents.

There are twice as many children as there are parents.

There are two teachers.

How many people in total will there be in the school hall for the play?   ⬜⬜

---

7   On Monday, the cafe sells four times as many cups of coffee as mugs of hot chocolate.

72 cups of coffee are sold.

How many more cups of coffee are sold than hot chocolate?   ⬜⬜

---

8   There are 48 dogs in the dog rescue centre.

$\frac{1}{6}$ of the dogs are terriers.

$\frac{1}{4}$ are golden retrievers.

$\frac{1}{3}$ are poodles.

The remainder are a mixture of different breeds.

How many dogs aren't terriers, golden retrievers or poodles?   ⬜⬜

/4

Circle the word which has the most similar meaning to the word on the left.

9	capable	compliant	competent	confident	complacent
10	hole	cavern	crypt	cavity	cubicle
11	behaviour	conduct	control	convoy	command
12	changeable	vulnerable	versatile	viable	variable
13	colossal	immeasurable	immovable	immense	amenable
14	famous	efficient	eminent	eloquent	evident
15	lucky	favourable	fashionable	forgivable	fortunate
16	ghastly	gruesome	fearsome	tiresome	loathsome

/8

 Circle the word which you would most associate with the word on the left.

17	picturesque	opinion	belief	view	notion
18	holiday	courage	luggage	haulage	message
19	ajar	door	wall	ceiling	floor
20	fish	series	gauges	scales	ranges
21	exercise	obvious	strenuous	various	riotous
22	court	effort	struggle	attempt	trial
23	relative	friend	neighbour	cousin	comrade
24	audible	mouth	ears	fingers	eyes

/8

Complete the passage by ticking the most appropriate word from the options.

25 ☐ bizarre
☐ ordinary
☐ exotic
☐ mundane

Nestling to the east of the Arabian Sea, Kerala is an   mix of coconut groves,

26 ☐ labyrinth
☐ tangle
☐ jungle
☐ riddle

wide beaches and a   of rivers. The eastern part of the state is hilly, but much

of the land is a flat plain. Blessed with a pleasant climate throughout the year, Kerala is a

tropical state with the coast running down its entire length and the towering Western Ghats

27 ☐ obstacle
☐ hurdle
☐ fence
☐ barrier

providing a protective   against the dry winds from Northern India. There are

28 ☐ frequently,
☐ annually,
☐ regularly,
☐ repeatedly,

two monsoon seasons   from June to September and October to November.

The temperature in Kerala rarely drops below 26°C, even in the winter.

29 ☐ placid
☐ fluid
☐ humid
☐ vapid

The sale of spices has dominated Kerala's trade for hundreds of years. The state's

30 ☐ abundant
☐ affluent
☐ creative
☐ fertile

climate and   soil provide the ideal conditions for producing spices like pepper,

ginger, nutmeg, cardamom, cinnamon and cloves.

/6

Practice Paper 4

 Clarence Birdseye

Born in New York in 1886, Clarence Birdseye was the sixth of nine children. From a young age he was only really interested in botany and zoology and after leaving school he began a college course with the ambition of becoming a biologist. However, by 1910, Birdseye could no longer afford his tuition fees so he dropped out and took a job with the United States Agricultural Department as a field researcher. The pay
5 was meagre and Birdseye was forced to supplement his income with fur trading.

In 1912, Birdseye embarked on a five-year fur-trading expedition to the Canadian peninsula of Labrador. During his time in the Arctic, he noticed that the local people froze vast amounts of fish during the dark, bitterly cold winter months because they found it difficult to source fresh food at this time. Birdseye learned how to fish under very thick ice, but what really intrigued him was what happened to the fish
10 after they were caught. He noted that once the fish were brought out of the water and placed on the ice, the combination of the temperature and exposure to the elements froze the fish almost instantaneously. The significance of this made itself apparent later when they came to eat the fish. To his amazement, Birdseye noticed that, once thawed, the fish were as firm and fresh as if they had just been caught.

When he returned to the United States, and with the help of a loan from his bank, Birdseye set about
15 inventing and patenting the world's first 'Quick Freeze Machine'. Birdseye developed and later perfected a system of packaging fresh food into waxed cardboard boxes and flash-freezing under high pressure. By 1927, his company was applying the same technology to preserve vegetables, fruit, poultry and beef.

The products were an instant hit and the company expanded rapidly, with frozen food products transported by refrigerated lorries to more and more shops. Today, commercially frozen foods are a multi-
20 billion-pound industry and the 'Birds Eye' frozen-food brand is widely sold all over the world. After a hugely successful career, Birdseye died a multi-millionaire in 1956.

Carefully read through the passage above and circle the correct answers below.

1 In which North American country is the peninsula of Labrador?

A. New York

B. Canada

C. United States

D. Mexico

---

2 How many younger siblings did Clarence Birdseye have?

A. Nine

B. Six

C. Three

D. Eight

/2

3 How old was Clarence Birdseye when he ended his college education?

    A. 22 years old

    B. 20 years old

    C. 18 years old

    D. 24 years old

4 What prompted Clarence Birdseye to seek extra work as a fur trader?

    A. He was interested in botany and zoology from an early age.

    B. He needed to top up his income from his job as a field researcher.

    C. He needed extra work in order to pay his tuition fees at college.

    D. He wanted to travel the world.

5 What caused the fish to freeze so quickly in Labrador?

    A. The Arctic weather conditions froze the fish immediately.

    B. The fish were so small that they froze very quickly.

    C. The local people had an industrial-sized freezer.

    D. The fish were put into small igloos.

6 From whom did Birdseye obtain the finance to develop his Quick Freeze Machine?

    A. Birdseye raised enough money by advertising for sponsors in the newspapers.

    B. His father lent him the required amount.

    C. Birdseye inherited a large sum of money from an uncle.

    D. His bank granted him a loan.

7 Which one of the following statements is true?

    A. Birdseye was over 80 years old when he passed away.

    B. Clarence Birdseye initially used foil cartons in which to package his frozen foods.

    C. Birdseye owned the patent to the Quick Freeze Machine.

    D. Clarence Birdseye was born in the province of Labrador.

/5

Write the answer to each question in the boxes below.

> Sophie's pencil case contains a certain number of felt tips, as detailed below.
>
> $\frac{1}{9}$ of Sophie's felt tips are blue.
>
> $\frac{2}{3}$ are yellow.
>
> $\frac{1}{6}$ are red.
>
> Sophie has just one green felt tip and no other colours in her pencil case.

8 How many felt tips in total does Sophie have in her pencil case?

9 How many felt tips are red?

10 How many felt tips are blue?

11 How many felt tips are yellow?

/4

 Circle the word which has the most opposite meaning to the word on the left.

12	**upbeat**	sarcastic	cynical	suspicious	pessimistic
13	**leisurely**	late	disorganised	hurried	scheduled
14	**meticulous**	untidy	careless	unwilling	frivolous
15	**dishevelled**	slack	shiny	smart	steep
16	**scarcity**	opulence	abundance	existence	presence
17	**volatile**	modest	discreet	calm	reserved
18	**understate**	denigrate	meditate	exaggerate	speculate
19	**jovial**	miserable	sociable	hospitable	deplorable
20	**vanish**	dissolve	materialise	diffuse	evaporate

/9

Complete the sentences by circling the most appropriate word from the options A to E.

21 Snowy owls have extremely thick _____, for insulation in the bitter winters.

A	B	C	D	E
beaks	bones	tails	plumages	claws

22 Many elephants die every year as they are _____ hunted for their ivory tusks.

A	B	C	D	E
reluctantly	relentlessly	reliably	reservedly	relatively

23 Snow leopards are so well _____ that they are almost invisible in a blizzard.

A	B	C	D	E
covered	hidden	coated	cloaked	camouflaged

24 Koalas have _____ to be able to eat plants that are poisonous to other animals.

A	B	C	D	E
evolved	emerged	expanded	eloped	excelled

25 Spinner dolphins are so called because they are able to _____ and turn in mid-air.

A	B	C	D	E
alter	stay	twist	shift	waver

/5

In each question below, the words may be rearranged to form a sentence. One word does not belong in the sentence. Circle the superfluous word from the options A to H.

26

spend	during	some	months	hibernate	the	animals	winter
A	B	C	D	E	F	G	H

27

peeling	ceiling	the	paint	drippy	bedroom	was	off
A	B	C	D	E	F	G	H

28

much	today	better	day	than	will	a	be
A	B	C	D	E	F	G	H

29

measure	cook	you	ingredients	out	correct	the	must
A	B	C	D	E	F	G	H

30

choice	snacks	hopeless	a	not	sugary	healthy	are
A	B	C	D	E	F	G	H

/5

Practice Paper 5

 In the following passages, some of the words are missing. Complete each passage by selecting the words from the options A to H. Each word may only be used once. Write the correct letter in each answer lozenge.

Passage 1

caught	prove	bay	make	blighted	fields	conditions	rapidly
A	B	C	D	E	F	G	H

The Sri Lankan tea industry began in the nineteenth century after the island's coffee industry was

(Q1 _____) by disease. The first tea plantation began operating in 1867 and the

owners soon realised that the combination of a warm climate and sloping fields created the perfect

(Q2 _____) for successfully growing tea leaves. The first shipments began to arrive

in London in the late 1870s and the public's thirst grew for the new beverage which was to

(Q3 _____) hugely popular and fashionable.

Tea production on the island expanded (Q4 _____) in the twentieth century. Vast

forests were cleared and plantation owners learned how to develop chemicals to spray on their

crops. These sprays kept the insects at (Q5 _____) and kept the tea plants

healthy. Plantation owners became very wealthy.

Passage 2

coppery	package	plucking	adequate	boiling	wither	sprout	process
A	B	C	D	E	F	G	H

Tea bushes are typically planted a metre apart and grow to around a metre in height;

(Q6 _____) rainfall is essential for growth.

The tea leaves are picked by hand every seven to fourteen days and the tea pickers are given daily

targets to meet: usually 30 kilograms. After (Q7 _____), the tea leaves are

taken to a factory where they are left to (Q8 _____) after having hot air

blasted over them.

The leaves are then crushed and they start to turn a (Q9 _____) brown colour

as additional heat is applied. Finally, the tea is separated and graded according to leaf size.

The entire production process is incredibly fast and it only takes 24 hours from the time the

tea is picked to (Q10 _____) it and have it loaded into bags ready for shipment.

/10

Tick the picture which is a 2D bird's-eye view of the 3D picture from the options A to D.

11

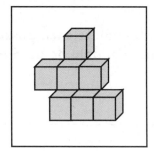

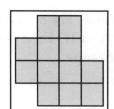
A

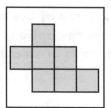
B

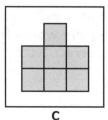
C

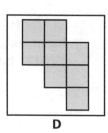
D

12

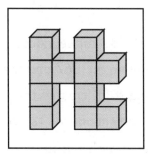

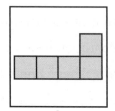
A

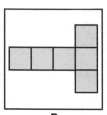
B

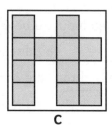
C

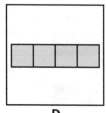
D

13

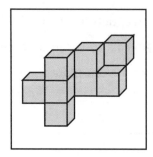

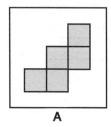
A

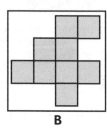
B

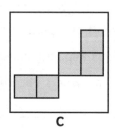
C

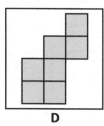
D

14

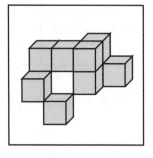

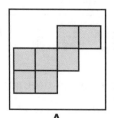
A

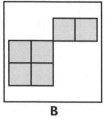
B

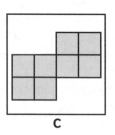
C

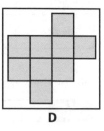
D

15

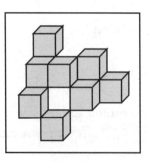

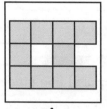
A

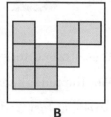
B

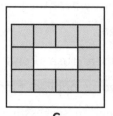
C

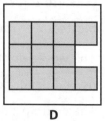
D

/5

In the following questions, circle the correct answer from the options A to E.

16 If 67 × 85 = 5695, what is 6.7 × 8.5?

A	B	C	D	E
56.95	5.695	569.5	5695	0.5695

17 How many thousandths must be added to 18.902 to make 19?

A	B	C	D	E
198	112	178	98	998

18 How many more hours are there in October than in June?

A	B	C	D	E
12	8	24	32	48

19 If eight identical T-shirts cost £79.92 altogether, how much does one T-shirt cost?

A	B	C	D	E
£8.99	£7.99	£10.99	£11.99	£9.99

20 One-quarter of a sum of money is £15. What is 50% of the sum of money?

A	B	C	D	E
£20	£12	£18	£15	£30

21 What is 35% of £320?

A	B	C	D	E
£112	£110	£108	£120	£118

22 $7x+2=y$ Find the value of y, when x is 4.

A	B	C	D	E
28	30	26	21	23

/7

Match the words to the correct definitions. Write the correct answer A to J in the spaces.

23	obnoxious	
24	haphazard	
25	perceptive	
26	courteous	

A worried and nervous

B very unpleasant and annoying

C eager to do something

D respectful and polite

E lasting a very long time

F quick to notice and understand things

G having a clean and tidy appearance

H dangerous and risky

I disorganised and random

J permitted by law

27	conference	
28	gimmick	
29	shortcoming	
30	replica	

A a system of writing that uses lines and signs to represent words

B something quirky, usually used to grab people's attention

C a principle or idea

D the line around a circular object

E a formal meeting for discussing ideas and opinions

F trust in your own abilities

G a badly damaged object

H an exact copy of something

I a situation where there is not enough of something

J a failing or a weak point

/8

Practice Paper 6

 Write the answer to each calculation in the boxes.

1   A train leaves Edinburgh with 117 passengers on board.

When the train stops at Leeds, 20 people leave the train and 17 people get on.

At Birmingham, twice the number of people who left the train at Leeds leave the train and 15 passengers get on. It then travels straight to Bristol.

How many passengers are on the train when it arrives in Bristol?

---

2   The ratio of vans to cars in a busy car park is 5:15.

There are 15 vans in the car park.

How many cars are there?

---

3   A cafe serves 43 breakfasts between 08:30 and 12:00.

The cafe serves 29 afternoon teas between 15:00 and 17:00.

The cafe's remaining customers all went for lunch.

If the cafe has a total of 112 customers all day, how many lunches does it serve?

---

4   Finn's car uses 1 litre of petrol every 8 miles.

In a week he drives 480 miles in his car.

How many litres of petrol does the car use?

/4

5 Elena is a florist and on Monday morning she has a delivery of 375 roses from her flower supplier.

She arranges the roses into bouquets with 25 flowers in each.

How many bouquets does she make?

6 Arjun needs to achieve a mean score of 12 points over the three courses of a cookery contest in order to qualify for the next round.

He scores 10 points for his starter and 9 points for his main course.

What must he score for his pudding in order to qualify for the next round in the competition?

7 Alice visits the train museum and sees that they have a selection of pencil sharpeners in the shape of famous trains.

All the pencil sharpeners are priced at 59p.

How many can Alice buy with a £5 note?

8 The number 42 bus passes the corner shop every five minutes.

The first bus goes by at 07:00.

How many buses will go past the corner shop between 07:00 and 08:38, including the first bus at 07:00?

/4

Circle the word which has the most similar meaning to the word on the left.

9	**critical**	casual	clinical	cynical	crucial
10	**height**	magnitude	altitude	longitude	latitude
11	**frantic**	irritated	devastated	agitated	disorientated
12	**amble**	saunter	slither	stagger	swagger
13	**lively**	cheerful	optimistic	animated	dazzling
14	**stir**	amuse	argue	accuse	arouse
15	**descend**	plummet	stumble	collide	pummel
16	**approve**	endure	enclose	engage	endorse

/8

 Circle the word which you would most associate with the word on the left.

17	**direction**	compass	protractor	microscope	thermometer
18	**sculptor**	portrait	picture	photograph	statue
19	**ship**	mariner	solicitor	aviator	tailor
20	**parachute**	submerge	descend	decline	emerge
21	**museum**	advert	alphabet	artefact	aqueduct
22	**fog**	cushion	blanket	pillow	towel
23	**accelerator**	slower	faster	wider	shorter
24	**book**	muscle	tendon	spine	lungs

/8

Complete the passage by ticking the most appropriate word from the options.

The giant panda, with its distinctive black and white coat, is adored all over the world and is

25
☐ speciality
☐ treasure
considered a national ☐ champion
☐ fortune

in China. So rare is the creature that today it is

26
☐ decrease
☐ dwindle
thought that there are only about 1600 left in the wild, and that their ☐ developing
☐ declining

27
☐ balmy
☐ booming
numbers is mainly due to the loss of their natural habitat. China has a ☐ bulky
☐ boisterous

economy and the continual expansion of the road and rail networks is destroying large areas

28
☐ reducing
☐ lowering
of forests which is ☐ subsiding   the giant pandas' access to the bamboo that they need
☐ slackening

to survive.

29
☐ trial
☐ test
Hunting remains an ever-present ☐ scare   to the giant panda, although poaching
☐ threat

30
☐ grim
☐ exact
the animals for their fur has declined slightly in recent years due to ☐ sharp   laws
☐ strict

and greater public awareness of the pandas' protected status.

/6

 Island for Sale

A rare opportunity has arisen to purchase an exclusive private island, with all amenities
in place to facilitate immediate occupation, just off the east coast of Tasmania.

The true tranquillity offered by Stanley Island would be difficult to find anywhere else in the world. The
island is located just 3km from the Tasmanian capital of Hobart and is easily accessible by boat, making
5   use of the beach which is on the sheltered eastern side. A short 90-second plane journey from Hobart,
landing on the island's private airstrip, is a faster alternative.

The 720-acre island is approximately 2km wide and roughly 4.5km end to end. It is large enough to always
offer something to explore, but without losing the small-island feel. Stanley Island is a haven for fishing,
swimming, snorkelling and relaxing; the island boasts a dozen stunning powder-white sandy beaches.

10   On the eastern side of the island, and with a breath-taking coastal view, is a delightful, spacious family
home. The house's 30 x 30-metre living room features magnificent solid oak furnishings, and the dining
room seats 12. The house has seven double bedrooms, three bathrooms, a large sitting room, an office, an
exercise room and a contemporary kitchen, fully equipped with the latest appliances. Located to the west
of the house is the caretaker's lodge, which enjoys stunning views over the Tasman Sea.

15   There is also a guest house, situated 800m to the north of the island's main property;
the guest house enjoys stunning views and comfortably sleeps four. The house commands
a weekly rental income of 2000 Australian dollars in the high season.

All three houses are self-sufficient, with solar power and rainwater catchments.
As a reminder of the island's grazing past, an old, large shearing shed is situated on
20   the west coast of the island.

Guide price: Australian dollars (AUD) $15,000,000   (£1 = 1.50 AUD)

Carefully read through the passage and circle the correct answers below.

1 What is the approximate area of Stanley Island?

A. 13km²   **C.** 12.5km²

B. 9km²   **D.** 19km²

---

2 Where is Tasmania situated in relation to Stanley Island?

A. Tasmania is to the east of Stanley Island.

B. Tasmania lies to the south of Stanley Island.

C. Tasmania lies to the west of Stanley Island.

D. Tasmania is situated to the north of Stanley Island.

/2

3 If new owners were to replace the flooring in the living room with tiles measuring
1 metre × 1 metre, how many tiles would they need to buy?

   A. 90 tiles

   B. 900 tiles

   C. 990 tiles

   D. 120 tiles

---

4 There are 240 acres of woodland on Stanley Island. What fraction is covered in trees?

   A. One-third

   B. One-quarter

   C. One-sixth

   D. Two-thirds

---

5 Which part of Stanley Island enjoys the most shelter from the elements?

   A. The west coast

   B. The northern part of the island

   C. The eastern coast

   D. The south coast

---

6 Which one of the following statements is true?

   A. It would cost over 10,000 AUD to rent the guest house for a fortnight.

   B. The main residence on Stanley Island can sleep a maximum of a dozen people.

   C. The electricity supply on Stanley Island is generated at a power station in Hobart.

   D. The main residence is located to the east of the caretaker's lodge.

---

7 What would be the price of Stanley Island in British pounds (£)?

   A. £30,000,000

   B. £15,000,000

   C. £35,000,000

   D. £10,000,000

/5

Write the answer to each question in the boxes below.

The distance graph below shows Lucy's progress in a 4-kilometre cross-country run.

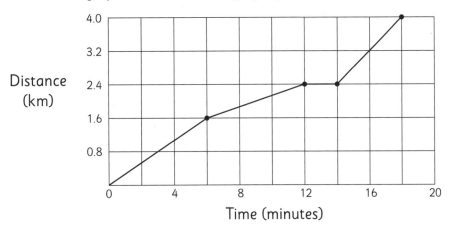

Distance (km) / Time (minutes)

8   How many minutes did it take for Lucy to run 40% of the total distance?   ☐☐

9   How many minutes did it take Lucy to complete the entire 4km cross-country course?   ☐☐

10   For how many minutes did Lucy stop and rest?   ☐☐

11   How many minutes did it take Lucy to finish the race when she started running again after her rest?   ☐☐

/4

Circle the word which has the most opposite meaning to the word on the left.

12	blossom	slacken	rumple	soften	wither
13	obstinate	inquisitive	determined	faithful	compliant
14	deceit	modesty	honesty	loyalty	humility
15	traitor	supporter	commentator	translator	survivor
16	recede	wander	advance	depart	detour
17	faultless	insufficient	incomplete	careless	defective
18	removal	transfer	installation	substitution	transmission
19	gorge	starve	soothe	scare	scrape
20	dribble	crush	trickle	deluge	cluster

/9

Complete the sentences by circling the most appropriate word from the options A to E.

21 Archaeologists glean information about the past by carrying out _____ , or digs.

A	B	C	D	E
mining	shovelling	excavations	drilling	tunnelling

22 Pharmacists prepare and _____ medicines that help people overcome illnesses.

A	B	C	D	E
bequeath	disclose	subscribe	administer	dispense

23 Architects design houses prior to them being _____ by builders.

A	B	C	D	E
formulated	constructed	established	organised	demolished

24 Conservationists work to _____ animals and the environment.

A	B	C	D	E
watch	assure	keep	protect	shelter

25 Journalists are trained to investigate stories and _____ people, often politicians.

A	B	C	D	E
interview	confer	discuss	audition	council

/5

 In each question below, the words may be rearranged to form a sentence. One word does not belong in the sentence. Circle the superfluous word from the options A to H.

26

were	the	porridge	menu	there	breakfast	on	was
A	B	C	D	E	F	G	H

27

a	fallen	were	had	road	tree	across	the
A	B	C	D	E	F	G	H

28

only	space	there	left	one	was	none	parking
A	B	C	D	E	F	G	H

29

was	all	over	above	scattered	the	debris	field
A	B	C	D	E	F	G	H

30

train	late	was	minutes	twenty	after	the	running
A	B	C	D	E	F	G	H

/5

Practice Paper 8

In the following passages, some of the words are missing. Complete each passage by selecting the words from the options A to H. Each word may only be used once. Write the correct letter in each answer lozenge.

Passage 1

concern	inched	outside	shape	tipped	surface	exciting	near
A	**B**	**C**	**D**	**E**	**F**	**G**	**H**

It is now over 50 years since Neil Armstrong became the first man to take a walk on the (Q1) of the moon. The dramatic moment came after he had (Q2) his way down the ladder of the fragile lunar module Eagle while his colleague Buzz Aldrin watched his every move from inside the craft.

The landing, on the Sea of Tranquillity, was (Q3) perfect and the very first words to be heard from the moon came from Buzz Aldrin: "Tranquillity base, the Eagle has landed."

Armstrong reported that they were all in excellent (Q4) and there was no need for any (Q5) for the astronauts' safety.

Passage 2

unveil	calm	historic	pressed	lunar	loud	mounting	signature
A	**B**	**C**	**D**	**E**	**F**	**G**	**H**

Back on Earth, in the mission control centre, tension was (Q6) as they nervously waited for news of a safe landing.

When the (Q7) landing was confirmed, one ground controller was heard to say: "We're breathing again." The astronauts spent two hours exploring their immediate area and they then gathered up a large selection of (Q8) rocks and other materials to take back home to Earth with them.

The men then proceeded to plant a flag and (Q9) a special plaque which contained American President Nixon's (Q10) and an inscription which read: "Here men from the planet Earth first set foot upon the moon, July 1969, AD. We came in peace for all mankind".

/10

Tick the picture which best completes the set on the left from the options A to E.

11

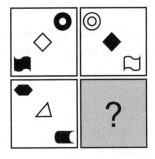

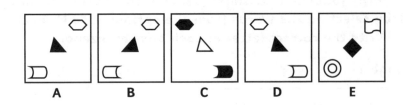

A   B   C   D   E

12

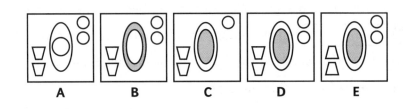

A   B   C   D   E

13

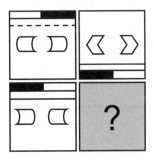

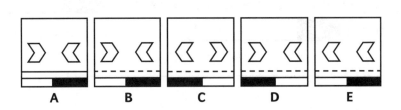

A   B   C   D   E

14

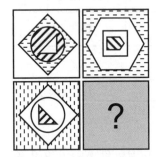

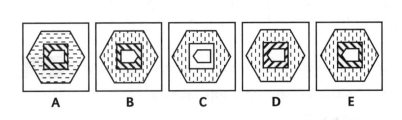

A   B   C   D   E

15

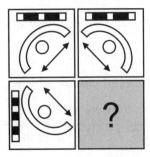

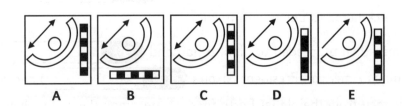

A   B   C   D   E

/5

In the following questions, please circle the correct answer from the options A to E.

16 Which one of the following numbers is divisible exactly by 6?

A	B	C	D	E
374	616	174	452	248

17 If 20% of a number is 35, what is the number?

A	B	C	D	E
105	120	140	125	175

18 How do you write the number 9 in Roman numerals?

A	B	C	D	E
C	IX	X	VIII	VIIII

19 Which of the following numbers is not a factor of 64?

A	B	C	D	E
6	4	8	16	32

20 What is the range of the following numbers? 140, 16, 22, 14, 1, 5

A	B	C	D	E
33	121	141	139	135

21 The mean of three numbers is 7. If two of the numbers are 2 and 11, what is the third number?

A	B	C	D	E
6	9	8	7	11

22 Increase £33.00 by 20%.

A	B	C	D	E
£49.60	£39.60	£36.60	£32.80	£39.00

/7

Match the words to the correct definitions. Write the correct answer A to J in the spaces.

23	discard	
24	forecast	
25	nominate	
26	neglect	

A   to prevent something happening by acting first

B   to fail to look after someone or something properly

C   to suggest that a certain person should win a prize or fill a job

D   to organise or arrange text on a computer

E   to throw something away

F   to punish someone

G   to find information

H   to predict what will happen in the future

I   to feel despair about something or someone

J   to publicly say that a person has done something wrong

27	widespread	
28	elated	
29	lavish	
30	absurd	

A   extravagant and generous

B   bigger than expected

C   happening in many places

D   positioned near the summit

E   extremely tasty

F   arriving later than expected

G   more than enough

H   very excited and pleased

I   very skilled

J   ridiculous and silly

/8

Practice Paper 9

 Write the answer to each calculation in the boxes.

1 When it opened on Monday morning, there were 12,048 books in the library.

On Monday, 440 books were borrowed and 44 books were returned.

On Tuesday, 39 books were returned and 78 were borrowed.

On Wednesday, 420 books were borrowed and 880 returned.

How many more books were in the library after it closed on Wednesday than when it opened on Monday?

2 There are exactly 400 students at St Mary's Primary School.

Ninety per cent of the students have school lunches and the remainder take a packed lunch to school.

Twenty per cent of the students that have school lunches are vegetarian.

How many vegetarian lunches are eaten each day?

3 The Kari family leave for their summer holiday on 27 July at 07:00.

They return home at 22:00 on 14 August.

How many nights have the family been away from home?

4 Tillie has an end-of-term geography exam.

She scores 86%.

The exam contained a possible 200 marks.

How many marks did Tillie lose?

/4

5 A flight from Dubai to Tokyo has one member of cabin crew for every 30 passengers.

There are 360 passengers on the flight.

How many members of cabin crew will be on board to look after all the passengers?

6 Lasvita has been fishing and in total she catches five fish.

She catches a carp, two trout, a minnow and a perch.

The fish weigh 550g in total.

The biggest fish is the carp, which weighs exactly half of the total weight.

The trout weigh 75g each, the minnow weighs 15g less than the perch.

How many grams does the perch weigh?

7 Joe has to catch a train at 13:20.

He leaves his house at 12:30 and spends ten minutes walking to the bus stop.

Six minutes later, the bus arrives and a quarter of an hour later Joe arrives at the train station.

The train is delayed by 14 minutes.

How many minutes does Joe have to wait for his train?

8 A florist is counting his unsold stock at the end of the day and he he has got five bunches of tulips left.

This is 12.5% of the total number of bunches of tulips that he had on sale that day.

How many bunches of tulips did the florist have for sale when he opened his shop?

/4

Circle the word which has the most similar meaning to the word on the left.

9	**suggest**	implore	imply	improve	impeach
10	**beastly**	cautious	capacious	calamitous	callous
11	**clutch**	creep	clamp	clasp	clash
12	**elastic**	flexible	credible	feasible	legible
13	**kindle**	invent	initiate	imagine	ignite
14	**dauntless**	feckless	fearless	flawless	reckless
15	**live**	reside	remain	rest	prevail
16	**examine**	scan	overlook	scrutinise	estimate

/8

 Circle the word which you would most associate with the word on the left.

17	**juvenile**	fox	foal	frog	ferret
18	**squash**	modify	reduce	disguise	dilute
19	**zest**	lemon	melon	pear	banana
20	**infamous**	patient	pirate	parent	pharmacist
21	**ancestor**	daughter	sister	grandfather	son
22	**paperback**	napkin	notion	novice	novel
23	**archaeologist**	exercise	excavate	expect	extend
24	**ship**	logical	optical	nautical	clerical

/8

Complete the passage by ticking the most appropriate word from the options.

A monarchy is a country which is ruled, or whose government is headed, by a king or queen.

In some cultures, this right to rule was, and in some cases still is, thought to have been

25 ☐ assumed
☐ admitted
☐ judged   by God. Throughout history, monarchs have enjoyed great powers and
☐ granted

26 ☐ submit
☐ introduce
have decided which laws to   ☐ disclose   and which taxes to collect. A monarch's right to
☐ entertain

27 ☐ rebellions
☐ resolutions
rule was first challenged by the people of France. In a series of battles and   ☐ rejections
☐ recessions

28 ☐ dictated
☐ executed
known as the French Revolution, the king was   ☐ depleted   and the country became
☐ terminated

a republic.

29 ☐ honest
☐ right
Today, there are still kings and queens, but few have any   ☐ real   powers. The
☐ sound

remaining monarchs fulfil a much more diplomatic role, representing their country in other

30 ☐ playing
☐ bowing
parts of the world, or   ☐ moving   as figureheads at events of national importance.
☐ acting

/6

Great Train Journeys

Often described as the greatest railway journey in the world, the 84-mile round trip from Fort William to Mallaig takes you past a list of impressive superlatives. Departing near to the highest mountain in Britain, Ben Nevis, it calls at Britain's most westerly mainland train station, Arisaig. The train passes close by the deepest freshwater lake in Britain, Loch Morar, and the shortest river in Britain, River
5   Morar. The journey terminates at the deepest seawater lake in Europe, Loch Nevis. Many travellers are attracted by the stunning view of the magnificent Glenfinnan Viaduct – which now appears on the reverse of Scottish £10 notes and is also famous as a location used in four of the *Harry Potter* films. The train offers the only remaining steam-powered service on the national network and the journey takes just a little over two hours.

10 The *Ghan* train takes its name from the people who came to Australia with their camels in the 1830s to help carry goods for natives venturing inland. They were from Afghanistan and were nicknamed 'Ghans' by the locals. The train's epic 1851-mile journey takes its passengers across Australia from the sweltering tropics of Darwin through the blistering red desert of Alice Springs to Adelaide. En route, the train first stops at Alice Springs, where the Pioneer Women's Hall of Fame pays tribute to the early settlers. Other
15 stops along the route include The Flying Doctor Service Museum, the World War I memorial at Anzac Hill and the opal-rich mining town, Coober Pedy, where the residents mostly live underground due to the searing temperatures.

The world's longest train journey takes place on the Trans-Siberian Railway. Departing the Russian capital, Moscow, trains snake their way through 5750 miles of the world's largest country. Upon
20 arrival in Vladivostok, passengers will have passed through eight time zones, a third of the world's total. The scenic highlight of the trip is Lake Baikal. This 400-mile-long lake is the oldest and deepest in the world and its crystal-clear water is populated by hundreds of species found nowhere else. The journey takes six days and among the basic public trains is the *Rossiya*, which is brightly painted in the Russian national colours of blue, white and red. For a truly luxurious train journey though, take
25 the privately operated *Golden Eagle*, which is equipped with the finest bone china, crystal glasses and classic silver cutlery.

Carefully read through the passage and circle the correct answers below.

1 Which is the deepest seawater lake in Britain?

   A. Loch Morar

   B. River Morar

   C. Loch Nevis

   D. Lake Windermere

/1

2 Which one of the following statements is true?

A. The Glenfinnan Viaduct is featured on the front of Scottish £10 notes.

B. The water in Lake Baikal is especially murky during the summer months.

C. Russia is the second largest country on the planet.

D. The *Ghan*'s first stop on its journey from is Alice Springs.

---

3 What makes the Fort William to Mallaig train service unique?

A. It operates the only remaining steam-driven trains on the national network.

B. It has a stunning view of the Glenfinnan Viaduct.

C. It operates on the shortest railway track on the national network.

D. Its trains stop at the most easterly railway station on the mainland.

---

4 Which one of the following statements is not true?

A. Lake Baikal is both the oldest and deepest lake in the world.

B. The *Golden Eagle* train is much more lavish than the *Rossiya*.

C. The colours of the Russian flag include white and red.

D. There is an impressive World War II memorial at Anzac Hill in Australia.

---

5 Which valuable gems are to be found at Coober Pedy?

A. Rubies

B. Diamonds

C. Opals

D. Sapphires

---

6 How many time zones are there in the world?

A. 8

B. 24

C. 12

D. 2

---

7 Why do the majority of the inhabitants of Coober Pedy live underground?

A. To protect their mines from smugglers

B. To avoid the thousands of tourists who come to gaze at them

C. So they don't need to get planning permission to build houses

D. In order to avoid the uncomfortably hot climate above ground

/6

Write the answer to each question in the boxes below.

The table below shows the number of visitors to a wildlife park on a single day.

10:00–11:00	11:00–12:00	12:00–13:00	13:00–14:00	14:00–15:00	15:00–16:00	16:00–17:00
48	56	68	58	?	54	?

8 There are exactly the same number of visitors to the park between 14:00 and 15:00 as there are between 16:00 and 17:00.

A total of 364 people visit the park during the day.

How many people visit the wildlife park between the hours of 16:00 and 17:00?

9 What is the mean number of visitors each hour?

10 How many more people visit the park after one o'clock than prior to that time?

11 Currently, the wildlife park can accommodate a maximum of 80 cars in their car park.

They have submitted a planning application for an extension to increase the number of parking spaces by 20%.

How many more parking spaces will there be after the extension?

/4

 Circle the word which has the most opposite meaning to the word on the left.

12 delicate	discerning	astute	capable	robust
13 artificial	essential	typical	unusual	natural
14 incentive	deterrent	interference	restriction	restraint
15 willing	repentant	resolute	random	reluctant
16 unfaithful	gracious	loyal	unselfish	courteous
17 thankful	inconsiderate	neglectful	ungrateful	forgetful
18 dawdle	harken	impede	hamper	hasten
19 calm	turbulent	impatient	insistent	persistent
20 repel	attract	disgust	offend	intrigue

/9

Complete the sentences by circling the most appropriate word from the options A to E.

21 Millions of people travel on London's _____ red double-decker buses every day.

A	B	C	D	E
important	model	standard	iconic	fitting

22 Gondolas are the traditional _____ of transport used in the city of Venice.

A	B	C	D	E
mean	tone	mode	plan	course

23 People mostly travel using husky-drawn _____ in countries above the Arctic Circle.

A	B	C	D	E
slabs	packs	trucks	sleds	ferries

24 Japan's bullet trains are famous for their _____ : all departing exactly on time.

A	B	C	D	E
luxury	acceleration	comfort	cleanliness	punctuality

25 In Kerala, exciting leisure trips can be _____ aboard houseboats made of wood.

A	B	C	D	E
endured	savoured	devoured	honoured	applauded

/5

In each question below, the words may be rearranged to form a sentence. One word does not belong in the sentence. Circle the superfluous word from the options A to H.

26

with	cutlery	cloth	laid	the	table	silver	was
A	B	C	D	E	F	G	H

27

a	flowers	beautiful	Roxanne	of	deliver	bouquet	received
A	B	C	D	E	F	G	H

28

drifted	along	a	off	Callum	sleep	deep	into
A	B	C	D	E	F	G	H

29

developers	built	a	property	bricks	estate	new	housing
A	B	C	D	E	F	G	H

30

was	on	moving	the	traffic	motorway	slowly	cars
A	B	C	D	E	F	G	H

/5

Practice Paper 11

 In the following passages, some of the words are missing. Complete each passage by selecting the words from the options A to H. Each word may only be used once. Write the correct letter in each answer lozenge.

Passage 1

most	never	not	reduction	hue	certainly	adorable	sharp
A	B	C	D	E	F	G	H

The Chinese dolphin holds a special place in the hearts of the people of Hong Kong. They are also popularly known as 'Hong Kong pink dolphins' and are so called because of their skin's rosy (Q1). The dolphins are playful and friendly and it's (Q2) uncommon for locals to see them leaping above the water or trailing behind fishing boats, scooping up any fish that slide off the decks.

But the (Q3) pink dolphins are in danger of becoming extinct, as they are being threatened by both the actions of fishermen and other people using boats.

In Hong Kong, there are no regulations controlling fishing and this has resulted in over-fishing and a (Q4) decline in fish supplies. This is causing a huge (Q5) in the natural food supply of the pink dolphins.

Passage 2

other	doubled	rise	boat	trial	congested	halved	increase
A	B	C	D	E	F	G	H

In recent years in Hong Kong, the waters have become more and more (Q6) with marine traffic. There are hundreds of high-speed ferries running daily between Hong Kong, Macau and many other cities in the Pearl River area.

In the past ten years, the number of boats has (Q7) and this has resulted in an (Q8) in the numbers of dolphins being hit and injured. Scars, probably caused by (Q9) propellers, can sometimes be seen on the fins or bodies of the dolphins.

Hong Kong is currently working to reduce the number of dolphins getting hit by boats with a (Q10) scheme where they provide the ferry owners with protective guards to be placed over their vessels' propellers to lessen the risk to the pink dolphins.

/10

Circle the picture that is a rotation of the picture on the left from the options A to D.

11

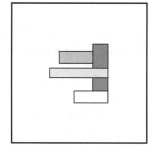

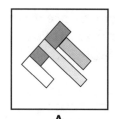 **A** 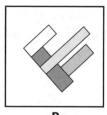 **B** 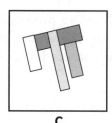 **C** 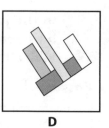 **D**

12

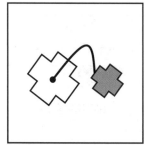

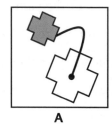 **A** 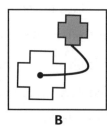 **B** 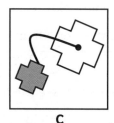 **C** 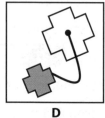 **D**

13

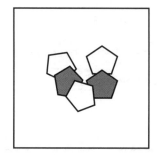

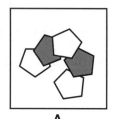 **A** 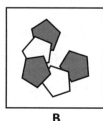 **B** 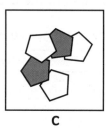 **C** 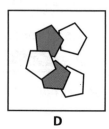 **D**

14

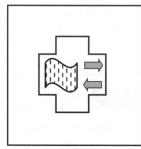

 **A** 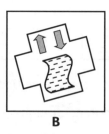 **B** 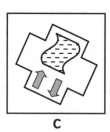 **C** 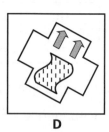 **D**

15

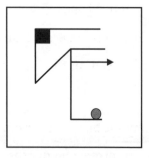

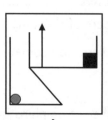 **A** 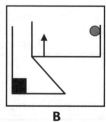 **B** 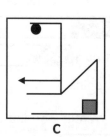 **C** 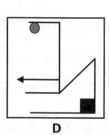 **D**

/5

In the following questions, circle the correct answer from the options A to E.

16 Which one of the angles below is a reflex angle?

A	B	C	D	E
49°	170°	95°	264°	116°

17 What is three-sevenths of 91?

A	B	C	D	E
39	28	31	35	42

18 Which one of the numbers is a multiple of 9, 5 and 3?

A	B	C	D	E
27	45	89	36	81

19 What is the mean of the following numbers? 24, 39, 42, 21, 14

A	B	C	D	E
27	25	29	30	28

20 If 5% of a sum of money is £6.00, what would 20% of the same sum of money be?

A	B	C	D	E
£20.00	£18.00	£40.00	£24.00	£120.00

21 What is the smallest number that can be divided by 7, 4 and 8, without a remainder?

A	B	C	D	E
1	28	56	36	49

22 How many minutes are there between 09:28 and 10:21?

A	B	C	D	E
47 minutes	53 minutes	49 minutes	57 minutes	51 minutes

/7

Match the words to the correct definitions. Write the correct answer A to J in the spaces.

23	capacity	
24	manoeuvre	
25	ration	
26	vitality	

A a written statement

B the amount that a container can hold

C the relationship between two groups or amounts

D a limited amount or a share of something

E a group of natural substances that are necessary for good health

F the ability to understand difficult concepts

G a challenging movement that requires skill

H an organised search for something

I liveliness and energy

J the situation where a person is imprisoned and not allowed to leave

27	fleeting	
28	renowned	
29	spontaneous	
30	patriotic	

A well known and famous

B strange and frightening

C not serious about a subject

D not lasting very long

E showing love of, and pride for, your country

F frightening or difficult

G not new, having been used in the past by someone else

H very pleasant to listen to

I thin and very easily broken or destroyed

J without previous thought or planning

/8

Practice Paper 12

 Write the answers to each calculation in the boxes.

1 Hattie got 27 questions correct in a maths test.

There were 50 questions in the test.

However, her teacher made some mistakes and had to re-mark all the papers.

When Hattie's test paper was re-marked, her score increased to 78%.

How many more questions did Hattie get right after her paper was re-marked?

2 A group of children go on a school trip.

The ratio of boys to girls is 2:3.

There are 70 seats on the coach and when all the teachers and children have boarded the coach there is just one empty seat.

There are four teachers on the trip.

How many girls are there on the school trip?

3 Gabriel earns extra money by writing recipes for magazines.

In March, he wrote 24 recipes.

In April, Gabriel wrote 25% more recipes than he did in March.

In May, Gabriel wrote 30% more recipes than he did in April.

How many recipes did Gabriel write in May?

4 On Monday morning, Mrs Cole asked the children in Year 5 if they wished that salad could be on the menu every day for lunch.

A third of the children present said 'yes'.

36 children said 'no'.

If two Year 5 children were absent that day, how many children in total are there in Year 5?

/4

5 Grace is on holiday and is staying in a hotel that has 42 floors.

Grace's room is situated on the 20th floor.

She enters the lift outside her room to travel to the top floor to admire the view.

However, instead of the lift rising to the top floor, it descends nine floors.

How many floors is Grace now from the top?

6 Hana has a patio in her back garden.

The patio is rectangular and measures three metres wide and four metres long.

She wants to replace the sandstone slabs with new, square, granite slabs with sides measuring 50cm.

How many new slabs will Hana need to buy?

7 There are 18 rows of chairs all set out in the village hall for a dance show.

There are 12 chairs in each row.

If 235 parents and 5 dance teachers arrive in the evening to watch the play, how many members of the audience will have to stand?

8 Florrie chooses one scoop of ice cream from a cafe that offers scoops of rocky road, strawberry or chocolate flavours.

She can choose to top her ice cream with toffee, chocolate or hazelnut sauce.

She also has a choice of chocolate flakes or sprinkles on top.

How many different combinations can Florrie choose from?

/4

Circle the word which has the most similar meaning to the word on the left.

9	agile	quick	nimble	clever	handy
10	bright	ominous	fortuitous	precious	luminous
11	amiable	friendly	ambitious	flighty	casual
12	dappled	striped	spotted	patterned	marbled
13	meander	entangle	crinkle	wander	squirm
14	mutiny	recession	rebellion	recreation	resolution
15	baffled	flattered	flustered	fixed	flummoxed
16	idea	notion	option	potion	vision

/8

 Circle the word which you would most associate with the word on the left.

17	political	parcel	party	pantry	park
18	raised	platform	pioneer	pastime	purpose
19	congested	melody	magazine	motorway	magnet
20	illegible	signal	sample	stirrup	signature
21	unfilled	verdict	vacancy	voyage	variety
22	editor	museum	machine	mansion	magazine
23	refectory	dance	discuss	dine	draw
24	doctor	parade	prescription	purse	plant

/8

Complete the passage by ticking the most appropriate word from the options.

The city of Dubai has a classic Arabian climate — blazing hot summers and warm winters — and

is home to the world's tallest building — Burj Khalifa. Inspiration for the

25
- [ ] impressionable
- [ ] iconic
- [ ] expressive
- [ ] inadvertant

tower came from the spider lily flower whose three petals are arranged around a central

cylindrical core. This same pattern is

26
- [ ] entertained
- [ ] embalmed
- [ ] embezzled
- [ ] embodied

in traditional Islamic architecture.

Building work began in 2004 and the

27
- [ ] landmark
- [ ] feature
- [ ] lookout
- [ ] square

tower was completed just six years later.

Construction workers

28
- [ ] appeared
- [ ] lounged
- [ ] laboured
- [ ] lasted

day and night, erecting a new floor every few days.

Burj Khalifa is a multi-purpose tower and within its walls are an

29
- [ ] luxury
- [ ] opulent
- [ ] boutique
- [ ] budget

hotel, luxury

residential apartments and chic offices. Visitors to the Burj Khalifa can enjoy a

30
- [ ] excellent
- [ ] unequalled
- [ ] highest
- [ ] panoramic

residents' library, restaurants and two swimming pools.

/6

Practice Paper 13

 Komodo Island and Dragons

The island of Komodo is situated 2400km to the north-east of Australia and has a population of slightly over 2000 people. The island is 30 kilometres long and 15 kilometres wide. All the residents of Komodo are descended from convicts who were transported there from other parts of South-East Asia between the years 1752 and 1863. The island has alternating wet and dry seasons. The first four months of the year are
5   the rainy season and for the remaining months of the year, Komodo enjoys a tropical, arid climate, with daytime temperatures rarely dropping below 30 degrees Celsius. Komodo is famous for having one of only seven stunning beaches in the world comprised entirely of pink sand, which makes it a very popular destination for tourists. The crystal-clear waters of the Indonesian Ocean are a magnet for visitors, who flock to the island to enjoy the snorkelling and diving.

10 The island is also notable for its population of Komodo dragon lizards, the largest and heaviest living lizards in the world. The Komodo dragon can weigh up to 70 kilograms and its body can reach up to 3 metres; their tails typically grow to be the same length as their bodies. The dragons prey on birds, rodents and other larger animals, such as wild pigs, goats and water buffalo, but their favourite prey is deer. These huge lizards are capable of consuming 80 per cent of their own body weight in one meal and their
15 metabolism is so slow that Komodo dragons are capable of surviving on as few as a dozen meals annually.

An ancient Indonesian folk tale recounts the story of a princess who once lived on Komodo Island. Legend has it that, once upon a time, the princess gave birth to twin sons, a human baby and a lizard baby, who lived together in complete harmony as they grew up. The locals still believe in this legend, and that the immortal princess returns to Komodo once a year to ensure that her many descendants are continuing
20 to live peacefully together. Local residents believe that this is the reason that the dragons – there are the same number of Komodo dragons as humans living on the island – are very rarely hostile towards them.

Carefully read through the passage above and circle the correct answers below.

1 What could be the maximum area of the island of Komodo?

   A. 90km²   **C.** 260km²

   B. 350km²   **D.** 450km²

---

2 What would be the maximum amount of food that the largest Komodo dragon could consume in a single feed?

   A. 60kg   **C.** 50kg

   B. 56kg   **D.** 70kg

/2

3   How often is the fabled princess said to visit Komodo Island?

     A. annually

     B. twice every year, in the rainy season and the dry season

     C. every month

     D. every time there is a full moon; roughly 12 times each year

---

4   What is the preferred prey of the Komodo dragon?

     A. rats and mice

     B. wild boar

     C. water buffalo

     D. deer

---

5   Which one of the following statements is true?

     A. Convicts were sent to Komodo Island over a period of 90 years.

     B. June and July are the wettest months on Komodo Island.

     C. Komodo's pink beach is one of only seven in the world.

     D. The number of Komodo dragons on the island is twice that of human inhabitants.

---

6   Which of the following three adjectives are found in the first paragraph?

     A. population, remaining, popular

     B. alternating, tropical, stunning

     C. entirely, slightly, descended

     D. transported, comprised, destination

---

7   According to the text, what makes the ocean surrounding Komodo ideal for water sports?

     A. The clarity of the water makes it a perfect location for water sports.

     B. The waters are very safe, even for weak swimmers.

     C. The water is very shallow; it is ideal for children.

     D. The waters are very warm.

/5

Write the answers to the calculations in the boxes below.

> A market stall has the following prices:
>
> Oranges 30p each   Carrots 49p per kilo
> Bananas £1.49 for four   Aubergines 95p each
> Plums 99p for six   Broad beans £2.00 per kilo
> Potatoes £1.99 per kilo   Asparagus £3.99 per bunch
> Cabbages 50p each   Leeks £1.85 per kilo

8 Amy buys four oranges, four bananas and a kilo of broad beans from the market stall.

How much change does she receive from a £10 note?   £ ☐ . ☐☐

9 Simon buys two bunches of asparagus and a dozen plums.

How much does he spend?   £ ☐ . ☐☐

10 Lena buys two kilos of potatoes and three kilos of leeks.

How much does she spend altogether?   £ ☐ . ☐☐

11 Tom buys four kilos of carrots.

How much change does he receive from a £10 note?   £ ☐ . ☐☐

/4

Circle the word which has the most opposite meaning to the word on the left.

12	**vivid**	dusky	dull	dismal	grim
13	**relegate**	determine	propose	promote	promise
14	**assemble**	summon	resemble	dismantle	disagree
15	**falsehood**	trash	truth	trick	truce
16	**income**	expenditure	outcome	outburst	expansion
17	**parched**	shrouded	misty	cloudy	soaked
18	**sever**	soften	select	seize	attach
19	**neutral**	collected	biased	detached	concerned
20	**taut**	supple	tired	loose	lax

/9

Complete the sentences by circling the most appropriate word from the options A to E.

21 Climate change has _____ in changes to weather patterns all over the world.

A	B	C	D	E
made	contributed	resulted	produced	arisen

22 Like all other _____ birds, ostriches have short wings and small wing muscles.

A	B	C	D	E
colourful	flightless	caged	exotic	wild

23 Some fungi can be extremely _____ and are therefore very dangerous to eat.

A	B	C	D	E
toxic	delicious	fresh	natural	cheap

24 Sound travels well through _____, so it is easy to hear when underwater.

A	B	C	D	E
solids	debris	sediment	liquids	steam

25 The internet can be a great _____ for information, but it can also be distracting.

A	B	C	D	E
reserve	refuge	resource	resort	retreat

/5

 In each question below, the words may be rearranged to form a sentence. One word does not belong in the sentence. Circle the superfluous word from the options A to H.

26

were	very	was	evening	August	warm	it	a
A	B	C	D	E	F	G	H

27

was	under	an	castle	a	there	tunnel	the
A	B	C	D	E	F	G	H

28

whom	haven't	vote	I	for	decided	to	when
A	B	C	D	E	F	G	H

29

to	with	need	water	you	squash	must	dilute
A	B	C	D	E	F	G	H

30

for	friendship	years	has	many	loves	their	lasted
A	B	C	D	E	F	G	H

/5

Answers

Practice paper 1
p.5

1	D
2	D
3	B
4	A
5	C
6	A
7	C
8	(7,9)
9	(1,3)
10	(5,7)
11	(7,3)
12	harmony
13	agreeable
14	optional
15	conclude
16	ignore
17	preserve
18	strange
19	harmless
20	obvious
21	C
22	E
23	A
24	B
25	C
26	E
27	G
28	C
29	E
30	A

Practice paper 2
p.9

1	G
2	B
3	D
4	A
5	H
6	E
7	C
8	F
9	B
10	D
11	C
12	D
13	B
14	E
15	A
16	B
17	C
18	E
19	B
20	D
21	A
22	D
23	D
24	H
25	B
26	F
27	D
28	G
29	B
30	I

Practice paper 3
p.13

1	56
2	48
3	30
4	90°
5	86
6	50
7	54
8	12
9	competent
10	cavity
11	conduct
12	variable
13	immense
14	eminent
15	fortunate
16	gruesome
17	view
18	luggage
19	door
20	scales
21	strenuous
22	trial
23	cousin
24	ears
25	exotic
26	labyrinth
27	barrier
28	annually
29	humid
30	fertile

Practice paper 4
p.17

1	B
2	C
3	D
4	B
5	A
6	D
7	C
8	18
9	03
10	02
11	12
12	pessimistic
13	hurried
14	careless
15	smart
16	abundance
17	calm
18	exaggerate
19	miserable
20	materialise
21	D
22	B
23	E
24	A
25	C
26	A
27	E
28	E
29	B
30	C

Practice paper 5
p.21

1	E
2	G
3	B
4	H
5	C
6	D
7	C
8	F
9	A
10	H
11	B
12	D
13	C
14	A
15	B
16	A
17	D
18	C
19	E
20	E
21	A
22	B
23	B
24	I
25	F
26	D
27	E
28	B
29	J
30	H

Answers

Practice paper 6
p.25

1	89
2	45
3	40
4	60
5	15
6	17
7	08
8	20
9	crucial
10	altitude
11	agitated
12	saunter
13	animated
14	arouse
15	plummet
16	endorse
17	compass
18	statue
19	mariner
20	descend
21	artefact
22	blanket
23	faster
24	spine
25	treasure
26	declining
27	booming
28	reducing
29	threat
30	strict

Practice paper 7
p.29

1	B
2	C
3	B
4	A
5	C
6	D
7	D
8	06
9	18
10	02
11	04
12	wither
13	compliant
14	honesty
15	supporter
16	advance
17	defective
18	installation
19	starve
20	deluge
21	C
22	E
23	B
24	D
25	A
26	A
27	C
28	G
29	D
30	F

Practice paper 8
p.33

1	F
2	B
3	H
4	D
5	A
6	G
7	C
8	E
9	A
10	H
11	A
12	D
13	B
14	E
15	C
16	C
17	E
18	B
19	A
20	D
21	C
22	B
23	E
24	H
25	C
26	B
27	C
28	H
29	A
30	J

Practice paper 9
p.37

1	25
2	72
3	18
4	28
5	12
6	70
7	33
8	40
9	imply
10	callous
11	clasp
12	flexible
13	ignite
14	fearless
15	reside
16	scrutinise
17	foal
18	reduce
19	lemon
20	pirate
21	grandfather
22	novel
23	excavate
24	nautical
25	granted
26	introduce
27	rebellions
28	executed
29	real
30	acting

Answers

Practice paper 10
p.41

1	C
2	D
3	A
4	D
5	C
6	B
7	D
8	40
9	52
10	20
11	16
12	robust
13	natural
14	deterrent
15	reluctant
16	loyal
17	ungrateful
18	hasten
19	turbulent
20	attract
21	D
22	C
23	D
24	E
25	B
26	C
27	F
28	B
29	E
30	H

Practice paper 11
p.45

1	E
2	C
3	G
4	H
5	D
6	F
7	B
8	H
9	D
10	E
11	B
12	D
13	C
14	B
15	D
16	D
17	A
18	B
19	E
20	D
21	C
22	B
23	B
24	G
25	D
26	I
27	D
28	A
29	J
30	E

Practice paper 12
p.49

1	12
2	39
3	39
4	56
5	31
6	48
7	24
8	18
9	nimble
10	luminous
11	friendly
12	spotted
13	wander
14	rebellion
15	flummoxed
16	notion
17	party
18	platform
19	motorway
20	signature
21	vacancy
22	magazine
23	dine
24	prescription
25	iconic
26	embodied
27	landmark
28	laboured
29	opulent
30	panoramic

Practice paper 13
p.53

1	D
2	B
3	A
4	D
5	C
6	B
7	A
8	£5.31
9	£9.96
10	£9.53
11	£8.04
12	dull
13	promote
14	dismantle
15	truth
16	expenditure
17	soaked
18	attach
19	biased
20	loose
21	C
22	B
23	A
24	D
25	C
26	A
27	C
28	H
29	G
30	F

Coverage Chart and Scores

	Practice Paper	Question number(s)	Page number(s)	Score
Comprehension	1	1 to 7	5 to 6	/7
	4	1 to 7	17 to 18	/7
	7	1 to 7	29 to 30	/7
	10	1 to 7	41 to 42	/7
	13	1 to 7	53 to 54	/7
Maths	1	8 to 11	7	/4
	2	16 to 22	11	/7
	3	1 to 8	13 to 14	/8
	4	8 to 11	19	/4
	5	16 to 22	23	/7
	6	1 to 8	25 to 26	/8
	7	8 to 11	31	/4
	8	16 to 22	35	/7
	9	1 to 8	37 to 38	/8
	10	8 to 11	43	/4
	11	16 to 22	47	/7
	12	1 to 8	49 to 50	/8
	13	8 to 11	55	/4
Antonyms	1	12 to 20	7	/9
	4	12 to 20	19	/9
	7	12 to 20	31	/9
	10	12 to 20	43	/9
	13	12 to 20	55	/9
Cloze	1	21 to 25	8	/5
	2	1 to 10	9	/10
	4	21 to 25	20	/5
	5	1 to 10	21	/10
	7	21 to 25	32	/5
	8	1 to 10	33	/10
	10	21 to 25	44	/5
	11	1 to 10	45	/10
	13	21 to 25	56	/5

Coverage Chart and Scores

	Practice Paper	Question number(s)	Page number(s)	Score
Shuffled sentences	1	26 to 30	8	/5
	4	26 to 30	20	/5
	7	26 to 30	32	/5
	10	26 to 30	44	/5
	13	26 to 30	56	/5
Pictures	2	11 to 15	10	/5
	5	11 to 15	22	/5
	8	11 to 15	34	/5
	11	11 to 15	46	/5
Definitions	2	23 to 30	12	/8
	5	23 to 30	24	/8
	8	23 to 30	36	/8
	11	23 to 30	48	/8
Synonyms	3	9 to 16	15	/8
	6	9 to 16	27	/8
	9	9 to 16	39	/8
	12	9 to 16	51	/8
Word associations	3	17 to 24	15	/8
	6	17 to 24	27	/8
	9	17 to 24	39	/8
	12	17 to 24	51	/8
Vocabulary	3	25 to 30	16	/6
	6	25 to 30	28	/6
	9	25 to 30	40	/6
	12	25 to 30	52	/6

Notes

Notes